MW00834837

No Way Out

by
Anne Schraff

Perfection Learning Corporation
Logan, Iowa 51546-0500

Cover Illustration: Carlotta A. Tormey

For information, contact
Perfection Learning Corporation
1000 North Second Avenue, P.O. Box 500
Logan, Iowa 51546-0500.
Tel: 1-800-831-4190 • Fax: 1-800-543-2745

Paperback ISBN 0-7891-5891-4
Cover Craft® ISBN 0-7569-1165-6
perfectionlearning.com
Printed in the U.S.A.

2 3 4 5 6 PP 07 06

1 Monique Grey was 16-year-old Aletha's hero. Aunt Monique was very different from her sister, Aletha's mom. Monique had been to almost every country on Earth. She had sung with a rock-and-roll band in her teens, and she had even once worked in public relations for a presidential candidate. She was just about the most interesting and fun person Aletha had ever known.

Mrs. Dunne, on the other hand, was a third-grade teacher at the local elementary school. Nedda Dunne had gone to college, married Aletha's father, and taught third grade until her three children were born. Then she had stayed home until Aletha's youngest brother was old enough to go to school. At that point, Mrs. Dunne had returned to teaching. Henry Dunne, Aletha's father, was about as exciting. The family did enjoyable things together like camping, but they rarely went farther than 100 miles from home. Now, on the brink of another mundane summer highlighted only by the usual weekend outings, family barbecues, and trips to the local pool, Aunt Monique had come to offer Aletha an exciting escape hatch.

"Nedda," Monique said to her sister, "I've just bought a brand new little pickup, and I'm anxious to get in touch with Mother Nature. I'm driving into the Sierra Nevada to spend a glorious two weeks communing with nature from a beautiful little resort there. I'd love for Aletha to come along."

Aletha had stared in wondrous disbelief at her glamorous aunt. Monique was seated on the sofa with her endlessly long legs crossed. Little golden chains encircled her ankles, huge golden earrings dangled from her ears, and a shiny diamond pierced her eyebrow. She was the fairy godmother who had come to rescue Aletha from dreadful boredom.

"Oh, Mom," Aletha immediately pleaded. "May I go? It sounds so cool!"

"Just a minute," Aletha's mom

answered in her sensible voice. "Just what do you know about the mountains, Monique?"

Monique waved her delicate right hand in the air, causing her many metal bracelets to clang like wind chimes. "What's to know?" she asked. "There's a lovely road leading into the mountains and a delightful resort on the lake. We'll just zoom up there, take a cabin, and spend our days watching the deer graze in the meadows. At the end of the day, we'll swim in the pool and soak in the sauna." Then she winked at Aletha as if it were a done deal.

"I don't know," Mrs. Dunne said. Her eyes moved back and forth from her sister to her daughter.

Aletha knew her mother had never totally trusted Monique. "Don't take this chance away from me, Mom," Aletha implored. "You *know* I'm bored out of my mind. Remember when you promised that if I got good grades this semester I could pick somewhere to go over the summer? I got all As and Bs! And I pick going to the mountains with Monique!"

"When I said that, I was thinking of letting you pick among summer camps," her mother said.

Aletha groaned. "I'm tired of summer camps. They're just a bunch of older college kids bossing you around. I've been to lots of summer camps, Mom. I want to go with Aunt Monique this year. It would be the coolest thing ever!"

Aletha's mom looked torn. Finally she shrugged and said, "Well, we'll run it past your father and see what he thinks."

Monique winked at Aletha again. This time the wink said, "We're on, kid." Aletha knew that Mr. Dunne was more easily charmed by Monique. He was the one who had said that Aletha could go with Monique to Australia two years ago when his wife had been totally against the idea. Mr. Dunne had also okayed the long weekend in New York City when Monique had taken Aletha to see five different Broadway shows. Now Aletha smiled at her aunt, knowing that the trip to the mountains was a sure thing.

****

Monday morning, Aletha and Monique packed their suitcases into the back of the glossy red pickup truck for the journey into the Sierra Nevada. The mountains formed a 400-mile-long spine that ran down eastern California. The resort they were headed for was in the most northerly part of the mountains.

"Oh, Monique, this is going to be such fun," Aletha said as they drove out of town and onto the highway. Her aunt did not like to be called "Aunt Monique." She said it made her sound old. "If it weren't for you, I wouldn't have *any* fun! Mom and Dad are so boring, and my life is just a total wasteland except for when you're around. If they hadn't let me go with you, I think I would have died of boredom!"

"Don't be too hard on your parents," Monique said. "Your parents might be predictable, but they've accomplished a lot and have built a stable home life for you. That's no small thing. Don't sell them short, Aletha."

"But I do love Mom and Dad," Aletha said. "They're just so dull!"

Monique chuckled. "Yes, my sister has always preferred traveling in the slow lane. Me, I like the fast lane. I was camping in the Himalayas while she was taking an extra algebra course. I was rubbing elbows with big-time politicians while she was doing her student teaching!"

"What's the name of that resort we're going to, Monique?" Aletha asked.

"Swiss Lake. There's a brochure in the glove compartment," Monique said. "Take a look at it."

A huge, lumbering camper crawled up the steep road in front of them. Suddenly Monique floored it, swerved around the camper, and then cut in ahead, shouting, "Wheeeee!" Aletha laughed. It was hard to believe that, at 36, her mother was actually two years younger than Monique. Nedda Dunne often acted more like Monique's mother. Not that Aletha's mother wasn't young looking and pretty too, but she was so cautious. Monique, on the other hand, was a free spirit. She did whatever she wanted to do whenever she wanted to do it. Aletha really admired that quality in her aunt. She had decided long ago that she would be just like that when she was in her thirties.

Aletha looked at the brochure. "Oh, this looks wonderful, Monique. The cabins are so cute. They're like little Swiss chalets!"

Monique nodded and said, "And it has a pool and a lake for swimming and a huge lodge for socializing. It even has a gift shop and a restaurant. I am really looking forward to walking barefoot in the grass and feeling the earth between my toes. I am ready to inhale fresh, clean air and look up at the sky and see the stars instead of city lights peeking out of a veil of smog!"

Just before nightfall, they reached a little motel called the Pine Grove. "Let's stop here for the night," Monique said, as if the idea had just struck her.

"Did you make reservations here, Monique?" Aletha asked.

Monique shook her head. "No need to. These little inns are never full."

Aletha noticed then that a blinking sign said "Vacancy," so she decided it didn't matter whether her aunt had made reservations or not. They spent the night there and in the morning gassed up the pickup and started the last leg of the journey to Swiss Lake lodge.

"Should only be a few more hours now," Monique told Aletha as they left the gas station.

As they drove deeper into the mountains, the scenery became more and more beautiful. Forests of pine trees towered above the road like cathedral ceilings. Birds flitted everywhere, and once Aletha saw a small fox scurrying off into the forest. Aletha and her aunt rolled down their windows to drink in the fresh, cool air.

"This is beautiful," Aletha said, taking a deep breath.

"Isn't it though?" Monique replied. "I can just feel Mother Nature all around us!"

But late in the afternoon, Aletha noticed the gas gauge was getting low. "Don't you think we should fill the tank again?" she asked.

"Oh, we've got plenty of gas," Monique replied, glancing down at the gauge. "This little truck gets great mileage. We'll just fill up when we get near the lodge. I'm sure there's a station around there. Trust me, honey. I don't buy gas until I'm down to the vapors! And I've never been stranded anywhere."

"Mom always gets gas when we're down to half a tank," Aletha said.

Monique smiled and said, "I can believe that. Your mom's never been one to take chances."

Aletha thought about that and decided it was true. When her parents planned a vacation, even a short one, they had the car checked over thoroughly by a mechanic. And they made a long list of things to do beforehand and items to take along to make sure nothing important was forgotten. Only then would they be on their way.

"You *did* make reservations for our cabin, didn't you, Monique?" Aletha asked as they climbed the twisting mountain road.

"Reservations? Honey, I *never* make reservations," her aunt replied. "You think I want to be stuck someplace I don't like? What if we get to Swiss Lake and we hate it? If I made reservations, we'd be stuck paying for the rooms, and then we'd feel like we had to stay."

"Oh, Monique," Aletha said. "The pictures look so nice. I'm sure we won't hate it. But what *would* we do if we don't like it?"

Monique shrugged her shoulders. "Gas up and continue on to another resort," she said. "Reservations are like marriages, Aletha. They can tie you down to big mistakes."

A slight look of sadness came over Monique's face then. For just a second, her lightheartedness fled. She had recently broken up with her longtime boyfriend, Bradley Simms, because he had been pressuring her to get married. Aletha could see that although Monique wouldn't admit it, she missed Bradley.

It was somewhat of a sore point between her mother and Monique that Monique was still single at 38. She had had a few chances to marry over the years but had always declared that she wasn't ready. Nedda Dunne had strongly approved of Bradley Simms, and she was disappointed when Monique had told her about the breakup. Bradley had treated Monique so well. He even had his pilot's license, and the two were able to fly wherever they wanted on a whim. Just the kind of thing Monique liked to do. To Mrs. Dunne, Bradley seemed like the perfect husband for Monique.

But Aletha thought the way Monique lived was wonderful. She drifted around doing exciting things, having more fun in a year than it seemed Aletha's parents had had in their lifetimes. That's how it looked to Aletha anyway.

Still, there were some times when you had to be sensible—like in making reservations ahead of time at what was probably a very popular lodge. Now Aletha asked, "But what if the cabins are all taken?"

"Now you sound just like your mother," Monique said. "You know, she spoiled every trip we ever went on when we were kids with her 'what-ifs.' 'What if it rains and we can't go to the beach?' 'What if we left the stove on at home?' 'What if we take a wrong turn and get lost?' " Monique chuckled over the memories. "Don't you be like that, Aletha. Be positive. There's going to be a cabin for us, the nicest cabin they've got. It's going to overlook the lake. And there's going to be a green meadow right out our window where all the deer come to feed at twilight."

Aletha smiled. Monique was right. Even though she admired Monique's carefree attitude about life, Aletha knew that she herself was becoming somewhat of a worrywart. Probably from being around her mother so much. She decided she'd try to keep a positive attitude for the rest of the trip. After all, she was on vacation with her favorite aunt. What could possibly spoil it?

Suddenly Monique said, "Whoa. There's a fork in the road coming up. I didn't see *that* on the map. I wonder which way we should go. Get out the map, will you, Aletha?"

Aletha removed the map book from the glove compartment and spread it open. "I don't see a fork, either." She turned the map over then and looked at the year it was published. "Monique, this map book was printed nine years ago," she said. "The roads might all be different now."

"Oh my," Monique said. "You could be right. No matter. I've got a good sense of direction. I know the resort is to the west, so it would make sense to take the road going northwest. Yep, that'll get us there for sure."

As they turned northwest at the fork, Aletha took another glance at the gas gauge. "I don't want to sound like I'm worried, Monique," she said. "But I sure hope we've got enough gas to get us there."

"There you go again, Aletha," Monique laughed.

"You're right. I'm sorry," Aletha said. She told herself that her aunt was a much more experienced driver than she was and that Monique would know when to fill the truck with gas.

At first the surface of the road heading northwest was fairly smooth, but gradually it became rougher as more and more potholes appeared.

Why hasn't anyone fixed these? Aletha wondered to herself. Then it hit her—the road hadn't been kept up because it was rarely traveled. The shoulder of the road was crumbling, and only a faint line could be seen separating the two narrow lanes.

"Are you sure this road will take us to Swiss Lake?" she asked Monique, trying to keep the doubt out of her voice. "Why would it be so full of potholes?"

"It's just the winter rains," Monique replied, carefully steering around the biggest of the potholes. "They wash out the roadbed all winter, and the crews just haven't repaired them yet. Summer's only just begun, you know."

Aletha glanced at the clock on the dashboard. It was nearly 5:30. They had planned on being at the lodge by now. But if anything, they seemed to be going into thicker forest. The road worsened by the mile, finally turning into not much more than a pair of tire tracks.

"I don't know, Monique," Aletha said. "We may have taken a wrong turn back there at the fork. I mean, there aren't even any other cars on the road. Wouldn't there be other cars headed toward the resort if this was the right road?"

Her stomach sank as she realized that the gas gauge was now pointing to empty.

"Going to be just around the next bend, honey," Monique said. She sounded cheerful enough, but as the little truck began to sputter, Aletha wondered if Monique felt as cheerful as she sounded.

2 "Don't you dare die on me now, truck," Monique threatened. "Just a little farther. You can make it."

But her threats were in vain. The truck continued to sputter.

"Monique, we're out of gas!" Aletha gasped.

"Calm down, honey," Monique said breezily. "It's not like we're trapped in the middle of the Sahara Desert or something! We're just temporarily delayed in a lovely forest. You yourself were just saying how beautiful it is."

"I guess it's time to use the cell phone, though," Aletha suggested nervously. It was true that the scenery was beautiful, but it was very remote there, and darkness came on quickly in the mountains.

"You're right," Monique said, opening her large purse. Aletha had never seen anyone carry as large a purse as Monique always did. "Now where is that thing?"

Monique mumbled as she dug around inside the bag.

"You're sure you put it in there, aren't you?" she asked cautiously.

"Of course I'm sure," Monique said. "I never go anywhere without my cell phone."

Aletha peered into the purse then. "What *is* all that stuff in there, Monique?" she asked.

Monique laughed. "My beauty aids, darling. I always carry spares in my purse. You wait until you're my age. You'll carry this many too." She began removing items from her purse and placing them on the seat beside her. "Let's see, here's my moisturizer, my eye cream, lip cream, toner, replenishing lotion, lip liner, lipsticks, hair spray . . ."

Monique continued to search in her purse, finally dumping everything out onto the seat. "Help me out here, honey," she said.

As she dug through the pile, Aletha realized she had never seen anything like it. A dozen lipsticks, numerous little bottles, mirrors, tissues, stubs from plays

Monique had seen years ago, change, tiny souvenirs, scribbled shopping lists, coupons.

But no cell phone.

Aletha couldn't contain her disappointment. "Oh, Monique, where is it?" she cried.

"Let me think," Monique said. She closed her eyes then. "I'll retrace my steps yesterday morning when I was getting ready. I packed my purse first. Then I packed my big suitcase with clothes. Then I packed my smaller suitcase with more clothes. Then I packed my overnight case with makeup and bubble bath and stuff like that. And *that's* where I put the cell phone. In my overnight bag!"

"Where is it? In the back of the truck?" Aletha asked hopefully.

"It must be," Monique replied. "Because I remember hauling the two suitcases to the truck, and then I went back in to get the overnight bag. I picked it up and headed out the door, but just then the phone rang. It was LaDonna Smith, one of the girls who used to be in our rock band. I hadn't heard from her in months. You remember I told you about LaDonna? She was the one who . . ."

But Aletha was already out of the truck, searching among the suitcases. "I don't see it!" she cried.

Monique got out of the truck then and looked into the bed of the truck. Suddenly she covered her face with her hands.

"*What?* What *is* it, Monique?" Aletha pleaded.

Monique laughed. "Your stupid aunt left the overnight bag on the kitchen counter—next to the kitchen phone. And it's still there with the cell phone in it!"

Aletha suddenly felt sick. "Monique," she groaned, "what'll we do?"

"Oh, now don't take it so hard," Monique said. "It's crazy mistakes like this that make a trip memorable. Years from now, we'll be laughing about it. Honey, every time we go somewhere, don't we have crazy adventures that we look back on and laugh over? Like when we took the wrong subway in New York. Remember? We got caught in that bad neighborhood? And all those rough-looking characters were about to have a rumble?"

"Yeah, I thought they'd shoot us!" Aletha said with a shudder.

"Oh, no. It was just like *West Side Story*," Monique said. "I expected those guys to break into song any minute."

"Well, maybe it was like *West Side Story* to you," Aletha said. "But I'm sure not looking back on it and laughing!"

"Come on, honey," Monique said. "And when we were in Australia, remember the wild dogs? I bet you've forgotten the Harbour Bridge and the Opera House in Sydney. But can you *ever* forget being chased by that little pack of wild dogs in the outback? Remember, we came around that little bend in the path and there they were. They were so cute!"

"Cute? I thought they were going to eat us alive," Aletha said.

"Well, it *was* a good thing that ranger came by," Monique laughed. "Remember that handsome ranger? He looked just like Mel Gibson."

"I sure wish a ranger would come along here," Aletha said. "No matter *what* he looked like."

Monique laughed again. "Now admit it,

Aletha," she said. "*Those* are the stories you tell your friends when you get back to school in the fall."

Aletha didn't say anything, but she knew her aunt was right. Very few of her friends could tell stories of the kind of adventures she had with Monique.

"Now you just quit your worrying, honey," Monique went on. "We'll just camp right here tonight, and in the morning someone will come along to rescue us. Someone always does."

Aletha looked around gloomily. Since the fork in the road, they had not seen a single car or truck. Why would anybody come along to help them on this deserted road? Aletha did not expect a rescue. "In the morning we'll probably have to walk out of here," she said.

"Honey, we're about ten miles up the mountain," Monique pointed out. "You must be joking if you think I'm going to walk that far. I didn't bring any shoes for that kind of strenuous activity."

"But we're here to commune with nature, Monique," Aletha said. "Didn't you expect hiking to be a part of that?"

"Honey, my idea of a hike is walking from my back door to my truck," Monique laughed. "I planned to watch the deer and walk barefoot in the soft meadow grass. And maybe even toss a few crackers to some chipmunks. But they'd have to be *nearby* chipmunks. I don't do hikes, Aletha.

"Speaking of crackers, though, I'm getting hungry. I thought we'd be sitting down to a nice, juicy steak at that lodge at Swiss Lake by now. Well, in the meantime, I guess some of those nutrition bars I brought will have to do."

Suddenly a strange look came over her face. "Uh-oh. The bars were in the overnight bag with the cell phone!" she said. "Did you, by any chance, happen to bring anything?"

Aletha remembered how impatient she had been with her mother when she had insisted on packing snacks and a few camping utensils in Aletha's suitcase. "Oh, Mom," she had complained. "They'll have all that stuff at the lodge."

"That might be," Mrs. Dunne had said. "But you never know when you might get stranded up there. Better to be overprepared than underprepared." Now she was glad her mother had been so insistent.

"As a matter of fact, Mom made me bring a bunch of snacks and bottled water," Aletha said. "She even packed some coffee and a small pot we use when we go camping. And she put in some matches *and* a flashlight. I saw one in your glove compartment too, so we have two flashlights now."

"Bless that levelheaded sister of mine!" Monique said, giving Aletha a hug. "But how are we going to make coffee? I don't see any electrical sockets in any of these trees."

"I'll make a fire," Aletha said.

"A fire?" Monique repeated in a bewildered voice. "You know how to make a real fire?"

Aletha smiled and said, "Sure. When my family goes camping, we take turns making the fire in the morning. Dad showed us all how. Go gather a few sticks, will you? I'll get some stones."

A few minutes later, Aletha had arranged some stones in a circle. Then she placed some small twigs in the middle and larger ones on top of those. Finally, she slipped a check from Monique's checkbook under the pile and lit it. The fire caught immediately.

"See? A *real* fire," she said proudly. While Monique went to look for a long stick, Aletha filled the coffee pot with coffee and water. When Monique returned, Aletha slipped the stick through the handle of the coffee pot.

"What on earth are you doing?" Monique asked.

"Take one end," Aletha instructed. "Now hold the pot over the fire."

Soon the pair had bubbling hot coffee to go along with their nutrition bars.

"This is wonderful," Monique said. "Hot coffee by our own campfire. I feel like a pioneer or something. I feel so . . . primitive!"

"When our family goes camping, we do all this all the time," Aletha said. "We never go to restaurants. We even catch fish and fry them."

"My, just smell the pines and feel the fresh breeze," Monique said in a dreamy voice. "Do you know this is my first real outdoors adventure? Tonight we'll be sleeping under the stars . . . just imagine." But then, as she thought about it, the smile left Monique's face. "But sleeping on what? The ground is so . . . so hard. At home I have a mattress that cost me a fortune. It's like sleeping on whipped cream. I could never sleep on hard ground, Aletha!"

For the first time since the truck had run out of gas, Monique looked distressed.

"We could sleep in the cab of the truck," Aletha suggested.

"In *that* little pill box? There's no room to stretch out in there," Monique replied miserably. "Besides, I can't *possibly* sleep sitting up. Why, my neck would be so cramped by morning, I'd *never* be able to see straight again!"

"We can make our own mattress, Monique," Aletha said cheerfully. Suddenly it was Aletha doing the cheering up, trying to raise Monique's spirits.

"*Make* a mattress," Monique cried in disbelief. "Oh, honey, now you're going too far. How could you make a mattress out here?"

"Well, it won't be a real mattress, but it'll serve the purpose," Aletha said. "All we do is collect pine needles and dried leaves and then sort of mound it all up in the shape of a pad. Then we tuck a sheet around it to keep all the material together."

"Sheet?" Monique asked. "Don't tell me your mother packed sheets too?"

Aletha laughed. "She was afraid they wouldn't change the sheets in the cabin often enough, so she sent me an extra. It'll come in real handy for our mattress. Let's start collecting leaves and pine needles before it gets too dark to see."

Monique still looked dubious. "But, Aletha, aren't there *things* in the leaves and the pine needles?" she asked. "I mean, insects, *bugs*! I couldn't possibly sleep, knowing they might come out and crawl on me during the night."

"Well, you wanted a wilderness experience, Monique," Aletha reminded her aunt. "So we've got to rough it a little bit."

"No!" Monique insisted. "I wanted to spend the night in a clean, luxurious cabin. I wanted to be lying between crisp white sheets at Swiss Lake. I didn't want to be sleeping on the ground with a bunch of horrible bugs!"

Aletha thought quickly. "There won't be any bugs," she said. "Insects can't live at high altitudes like this." Aletha knew that wasn't so, but she had to say something to calm Monique down.

"Oh, is that right? I didn't know that," Monique said with relief. "You are so clever, Aletha!"

Monique and Aletha quickly gathered enough pine needles and leaves to make a nice mound. Then Aletha spread the sheet over the mound and tucked it in at the edges. Finally she tried lying on the mattress.

"Oh, Monique, it's great," she said. "It's really comfortable. Try it. It feels almost like a real mattress. It's not bad at all."

It was twilight now, and Monique looked down at the pad. "I suppose it will have to do," she said. "Should we change into our pajamas?"

"I don't think so," Aletha said, hiding a smile. "We'd better save our pajamas for when we get to Swiss Lake and sleep in real beds."

"Oh, Aletha," Monique moaned, "I *always* take a shower, a nice *hot* shower, before I go to bed. I feel so dirty right now! Absolutely filthy!"

"But we're not really that dirty, Monique," Aletha pointed out. "We showered at the motel this morning, and we've only been driving all day."

"I always shower in the morning *and* in the evening," Monique said, a pained look on her face. "I just feel so . . . so unclean!"

Aletha hid her smile again. She thought it was a good thing Monique was born in modern times. She would have made a pretty poor pioneer!

3 Both Aletha and her aunt lay down on the sheet-covered mound then. They didn't have blankets, so they covered themselves with clothing from the suitcases. Aletha lay under her jacket, and Monique was covered with her lovely white angora sweater.

When Aletha glanced over at Monique, she could see that her eyes were closed and that she was just drifting off. Aletha closed her eyes, too, thinking about how they were making the best of the situation, when Monique let out a gasp. Suddenly she was on her feet, screaming. She hurled her sweater violently away from her.

Aletha scrambled to her feet. "Monique! What's wrong? Are you okay?" she cried.

Monique was shaking, "Oh! This hideous, poisonous spider was crawling on my sweater. It was almost at my throat! In another minute it would have been on my skin, sinking its deadly fangs into my veins! Oh, Aletha! You said there were no insects up here!"

Aletha walked over to where Monique had thrown the sweater. She saw a small, brown spider scurrying off the sweater and into the dirt.

"It was just a harmless little spider," Aletha said. "Technically, spiders aren't insects, Monique. They're arachnids. I think it was probably more afraid of you than you were of it."

"*That* is not possible," Monique said. "And don't give me that scientific mumbo jumbo! It's a bug, and that's all there is to it! I am *not* spending another minute sleeping outside with all of those horrible creatures. I'm going into the cab of the truck."

"But you said you wouldn't be able to sleep sitting up in that dinky little cab, Monique," Aletha reminded her.

"I don't care," Monique said huffily. "I am *not* being eaten alive by giant bugs!" She marched toward the truck. Then she looked back and said, "And if you had any sense, you'd come into the cab too!"

"I don't mind a few little spiders," Aletha replied. "When I go camping with Mom and Dad, there are always bugs around. I'm used to it. I can't sleep sitting up, either."

"Suit yourself, but if there are any more of those arach—"

"Arachnids," Aletha said.

"What*ever*!" Monique said impatiently. "Anyway, if there are any more of those things around, you can be sure they'll be crawling all over you during the night! They are the most bloodthirsty creatures I have *ever* seen!"

"If that happens, I'll come into the truck," Aletha promised. She hid a smile from Monique.

Aletha lay back down on the makeshift mattress. She thought back to the time the wild dogs had chased Monique and her in Australia. It had happened a little differently than the way Monique remembered it. They were supposed to stay on the marked trail. Everybody else did. But being the free spirit she is, Monique wanted to explore where the tourists were not supposed to go. She was sure there was something they weren't supposed to see. She had convinced Aletha to take a little path off the trail.

Now, recalling the incident, Monique could laugh about it, but at the time the wild dogs appeared, she had been hysterical. She was sure those dogs would eat her alive. She kept wailing that she had never hurt a wild dog, so why did the whole pack have it in for her? Her wailing, in fact, is what brought the park ranger their way. He had thought an animal was injured. Aletha chuckled quietly to herself then. No, Monique did not do well out in the wilderness.

Aletha lay awake, staring up at the stars for a while. She liked being outdoors. She simply got tired of going to the same places year after year.

Aletha wasn't really worried yet about the present predicament. They were only about ten miles from the wrong fork they had taken. Since the other road must have been the way to Swiss Lake, that meant they were not all that far from the resort. If worse came to worst, she was sure she could make the ten-mile walk back to the fork in the road. At home, she loved to walk and thought nothing of going five miles in an afternoon. Then, no doubt, she could hail one of the cars headed for Swiss Lake, and the passengers would send for help. Swiss Lake looked like such a nice resort that there had to be a lot of other people going there too.

But the more Aletha thought about it, the more uneasy she became. Disturbing little details came into her mind. On the long trip into the San Felipe Mountains, they had come across very little traffic. During the last five miles before the fork in the road, there had been no cars at all. Why hadn't other cars been heading for the fork and then the road leading to Swiss Lake? This was the beginning of summer, and the weather was beautiful. Where were all the people? It seemed that most of the traffic had turned off about five miles before the fork.

It had not struck Aletha as strange at the time, but now she wondered about it. Why weren't even delivery trucks going to Swiss Lake? Where was everybody? It was almost as if there was nothing worth going to beyond the intersection.

But still, Aletha told herself, they weren't in any real danger. What if Aletha did have to walk 15 miles back to the last place they saw traffic? She could hail a passing car from there. Besides, she had promised to call home the minute they were settled in at Swiss Lake. Tonight, when Aletha did not call, her parents would be alerted that something was wrong. They might call the resort and find out that Aletha and Monique had not checked in. Then they would certainly start a search. The thought comforted Aletha. Maybe there was a rescue vehicle already on the way!

Aletha finally drifted off to sleep but not for long. She opened her eyes to see Monique kneeling on the ground beside her.

"I can't sleep," Monique was complaining. "I tried to sleep in the cab, but you were right. It's so cramped and miserable!"

"Oh, Monique, come lie down here," Aletha said. "All the spiders have probably gone to sleep. I don't think any will bother you now. It's too late."

"It's not just that," Monique said. "I've been thinking. Your parents don't even know where we are!"

Now Aletha was wide awake. "Of course they do! You said you'd given them a copy of the brochure for Swiss Lake. Remember when you gave them that manila envelope with the brochure in it?"

"I meant to, but I didn't," Monique said. "I mean, I gave them an envelope, but it was the wrong one. I just found the envelope with the brochure in it in the truck. The one I gave your mom and dad must've been just some stuff about my new truck that I brought along to read— warranty information and maintenance schedules. I gave your parents the wrong envelope. Oh, I know it! Don't say it, Aletha. I don't blame you for hating me!"

"I don't hate you, Monique," Aletha assured her aunt. "I was just so glad that Mom and Dad knew about Swiss Lake. I thought when we didn't register there, they'd send out a search party. But at least they know we're in the Sierra Nevada. I mean, how many resorts can there be in these mountains? I bet Swiss Lake is one of the biggest. So they'll just start calling all the resorts and asking if we've registered . . ." Aletha's voice trailed off then as it dawned on her that Aletha and Monique were not registered at Swiss Lake—or anywhere else!

Monique's voice in the darkness was full of regret. "I am such an idiot. I know I screwed up big-time."

"But there can't be many resorts in these mountains, can there . . . ?" Aletha asked hopefully.

Monique sighed. "I don't know that for sure, but these mountains run for hundreds of miles. I have a feeling it would be like looking for a needle in a haystack. Oh, Aletha, I am so ashamed of myself. You must think I'm a total airhead. First I forget the cell phone, and then I take a wrong turn. And now it turns out that I didn't even give your parents the right envelope!"

Don't forget about running out of gas, Aletha thought to herself. But after all the wonderful times her aunt had given her, Aletha thought she should cut Monique some slack. She smiled weakly and said,

"It's okay. We'll be okay."

"You're a darling to be so forgiving," Monique said. "But what will we do now?"

"I was thinking that I could just start walking down the road when it gets light," Aletha said. "And when I come to where there's some traffic, I'll hail a car and they'll send for help."

"You're talking about hiking ten miles *alone*?" Monique gasped.

"I can do it, Monique," Aletha said. "I'm a good walker. I've been in a lot of these walkathons for charities, and Mom and I usually walk two miles every night. You can wait here for me, and I'll send help."

"Oh, Aletha, I couldn't let you do that," Monique said. "You're only 16 years old. I'm supposed to be the adult here. I'm supposed to be looking after you! What if you're attacked by a wild animal?"

"I don't think there are any dangerous wild animals around here," Aletha said. "I think there are just squirrels and maybe deer."

"Wait," Monique said. "I'll get the brochure for Swiss Lake and see what it says about wildlife in the area."

Monique went to the truck and got the brochure. She came back and began to read it by the light of the flashlight she had taken from the glove compartment. " 'The cool pine and red fir forests provide shelter for all kinds of wildlife including grouse, porcupines, and golden ground squirrels.' "

"See?" Aletha broke in triumphantly. "It sounds like there's nothing around here but cute little harmless animals."

But Monique continued reading. " 'Mule deer are very common and can be seen grazing at twilight and in the early morning. Feeding of any wild animal should be avoided, but it is especially important to avoid any contact with the large brown bears that sometimes appear near campsites. Keep all food in tightly closed containers to avoid attracting these animals. Although bear attacks are rare, sometimes a hungry bear will come very close to a campsite and, under certain circumstances, attack a human, inflicting serious or fatal injuries. In the past two decades, two hikers have been killed by bears.' Oh, Aletha! I was right! It is dangerous around here. If you go walking alone, you could be attacked by a bear!"

"But, Monique, they said it was rare," Aletha said. Still, in her heart, she dreaded the long walk through the forest, now that the subject of bears had been raised. She remembered reading about occasional bear attacks at campgrounds over the last several years.

"No, we shouldn't panic," Monique announced firmly. "We should just sit tight right here and wait for someone to come and rescue us. Or—" her eyes lit up. "We could signal for help with our flashlights! Yes! We could turn our flashlights on, and if a plane is flying low overhead, the pilot will see the unusual lights and come investigate!"

"Monique, have you seen or heard any planes since we've been here?" Aletha asked.

"Well, no, but that doesn't mean some pilot might not just take a spin over the mountain and spot us," Monique replied. "Bradley was always flying around just for fun. Once he decided I should see the Grand Canyon, and a little while later we were there! Another time he took me over Los Angeles at night. It was the most beautiful sight I have ever seen. A river of lights! It was so romantic! Bradley was always flying around."

Monique walked a few feet away to where there were no trees above. Then she shone her flashlight into the air. "There!" she said.

"Monique, I don't think anybody in the sky could see a light like that," Aletha said. "That's a pretty weak beam."

"Well, then, I'll just put fresh batteries in the flashlight so it's brighter," Monique said in a spirited voice. "Where there's a will, there's a way. I *always* carry spare batteries for my flashlight." She marched back to the pickup, was gone a few minutes, and returned, crestfallen. "I forgot to put extra batteries in the glove compartment when I bought this new truck. Do you have any, Aletha?"

Aletha shook her head in the darkness. Somehow she was not surprised. "I have a couple of batteries, but I don't want to waste them," she said. "There might come a time when we really need them. But I have an idea. We'll build another fire. That'll be a lot easier to spot from the sky than a couple of little flashlight beams. It's going to be dawn soon anyway, and we'll need a fire to heat our coffee. So I'll just build one now."

In a short time Aletha had a good-sized fire going. She heated some bottled water, and they used it to wash their faces. Monique got her purse and took out her compact mirror. She held it in front of her with one hand and shined the flashlight on it with the other.

"Look at my face!" she moaned. "It looks terrible—like I'm 90 years old! I didn't put my special conditioning cream on last night. And now just look at me! I look like an old maid."

"You look fine, Monique," Aletha said.

"That's easy for you to say, honey," Monique replied, dabbing her face with lotion. "You've got the bloom of youth in your cheeks. You're beautiful no matter what you do or don't do. I'm more than twice your age. I need all the help I can get."

Suddenly Aletha heard a strange sound.

At first she thought it might be an airplane in the distance, and her hopes soared. But then another similar sound came, a low rumble, and there was a flash of light in the sky.

"Lightning!" Aletha said.

A new fear crawled into her heart. When it rained hard in the mountains, flash floods often followed. On uneven terrain like this, instant waterfalls and sudden rivers appeared practically out of nowhere. What if really heavy rain came down and washed out the campsite?

4 Aletha and Monique climbed into the cab of the truck. "I guess we should try to get some sleep until the storm passes," Monique said.

"I'll try," said Aletha as she lay her head on the back of the seat.

The pair slept for a few hours. When Monique woke up, she saw that it had only sprinkled so far. She turned on the radio. A few minutes later, a weather report came on: *Thunderstorms will be moving into the area later today, becoming heavy toward morning.*

"Monique," Aletha said, "they just said the rain isn't going to get heavy until tomorrow. That means I've got time to make it to the highway when the sun comes up, but I've got to go today! I've got to try!"

"No!" Monique insisted. "It's too dangerous. I've been thinking. Those two roads at the fork branched off but not too sharply. They looked almost parallel. If the other road was the right one, it means that Swiss Lake is just east of here. Maybe only a couple of miles."

"You might be right," Aletha said hopefully, liking the idea. "If we head due east, we might just reach the resort. But what about your feet? Can you walk that far?"

"My little tennis shoes will just have to do," Monique said. "I just know I'm *not* going to let you wander through these mountains alone. If your mother found out, she'd *never* let me take you anywhere again! Anyway, if we head out right after breakfast, we could be to Swiss Lake in time for lunch!"

Aletha nodded. She didn't feel as confident as Monique, but it was worth a try.

Before eating their meager breakfast of nutrition bars and coffee again, they moved the suitcases and all their clothing into the truck to protect it from the rain. After breakfast, they put out their fire and started walking east.

When they got to a clearing, Aletha

glanced up at the sky. She didn't hear any lightning now, but she saw a few little clouds in the distance. None looked very threatening though. But she knew that little clouds had a way of gathering together, forming huge cumulonimbus clouds that could bring heavy downpours. She could see that it wouldn't happen for several hours though, and by then maybe they would be at Swiss Lake.

The trail wasn't easy as the pair moved east. They had to struggle through thistles and brush, and scramble up and down crumbling slopes. Aletha's athletic shoes supported her fairly well, but Monique's pretty little tennis shoes with the pink rhinestones did little to protect her feet.

After about a mile, Monique began complaining that her feet hurt. For her sake, they stopped and rested now and then, but Aletha was anxious to keep going. If they didn't find the resort, she knew they had to get back to the campsite and be inside the truck before the rains came.

About a mile later, Monique sat down heavily on a fallen log. "Honey, I'm not sure how much farther I can go," she said, slipping off her shoes and rubbing her feet.

Aletha stared at the endless forest of trees ahead of her. If Swiss Lake was just around the bend, she saw no evidence of it from there. She saw no sign of a road up ahead or even any paths or hiking trails. Aletha began to worry that maybe this walk had been a big mistake. Maybe all they were doing was putting distance between themselves and the pickup truck. And if the rains came early, that could be disastrous.

"Tell you what, Monique," she said. "You rest here for a while, and I'll go up ahead a little ways and see if I can make out any sign of the resort. I won't go very far, I promise."

Monique seemed relieved by the suggestion. "Oh, I *am* exhausted. It would be nice to just sit down for a little while." But suddenly her eyes were filled with fear. "But what about bears, Aletha? What if one attacks you? Or attacks *me*? What would I do all alone here?"

"I'm sure there aren't any bears around

here," Aletha said, trying to sound confident. "I mean, we haven't seen any so far."

Monique looked around nervously. "Maybe," she said in a trembling voice. "But you'll come right back, won't you? I mean, you won't get lost or forget where I am? Because if you did, I don't know what I would do. I mean, I'm not even sure I could find my way back to the truck, my brain is so addled by this whole experience."

So much for her good sense of direction, Aletha thought. She was beginning to realize a few things about her aunt. Compared to Aletha's mother, Monique had always seemed so self-sufficient, so confident. She had always been the brave sister, the one who ventured unafraid into new challenges. Nedda Dunne had always been the timid one. The one who measured all the odds before making a move.

But now Monique seemed really frightened. She was a grown woman, and she was looking for reassurance from her teenage niece. She was almost helpless.

Aletha wondered what her mother would do in this situation. To start with, she'd have never run out of gas. And her mother would have remembered the cell phone. She would have let someone know exactly where they were going. And she'd have *never* brought along a pair of rhinestone tennis shoes! Her mother would have dotted all her *i*'s and crossed all her *t*'s, that's for sure! Aletha was beginning to appreciate her mother more.

"I'll remember where you are, Monique," Aletha promised. "And I won't be long either. I'll be back in no time whether I find anything or not."

"Hurry," Monique pleaded, looking around fearfully again. "And be careful."

"I will," Aletha said, starting out.

Once freed of having to allow for Monique's slower pace, Aletha moved more rapidly through the forest. As she walked, she stared into the distance, eager for the smallest sign that the resort was near. She hoped to see a trail or some hikers. The brochure had said they even had horseback rides through the forest. She glanced around, looking for evidence of horse droppings, indicating that riders had come through in recent days. But there was nothing.

Aletha walked another mile and a half but still saw no sign of Swiss Lake or any human habitation. But now she began seeing something else. The beautiful green of the forest was gradually giving way to the ugly spectacle of burnt ground. Many of the trees were mere skeletons, thrusting their bony, scorched branches out as if pleading for help.

Aletha knew there had been a recent fire here, maybe last fall. It had been one of those terrible forest fires that roared over the land, burning everything in its path. Every summer and fall such fires occurred in these mountains. Aletha would hear about them on television, but they never really touched her life, so she didn't pay much attention. The fires were just another news story.

Looking around, Aletha could see small green plants rising up from the blackened earth. She knew the forest floor was making a comeback. But the large trees were all dead. The landscape looked like a

disaster-torn city. Aletha could still smell
the fire, more intensely now because of
the humidity the impending rains were
bringing with them.

Aletha continued on for a while and
then glanced at her watch. It was almost
noon, and she had seen no sign of Swiss
Lake. No people. Not even any animals.
Obviously, the forked roads were not
parallel as Monique and Aletha had hoped.
The roads started out close together, but
then they ranged far apart.

Aletha sat down on a rock. Tears came
to her eyes. Now they really *were*
stranded. A series of seemingly small
mistakes had quickly caused their little
carefree getaway to become a dangerous
situation.

Monique's flippant attitude about
nature had been wrong. One simply didn't
"zoom" up a mountain, watch deer grazing
serenely in meadows, and walk barefoot
through the grass. Nature in these
mountains was a force to be reckoned
with. A force that could seldom be
outsmarted and rarely be outrun.

Aletha dried her tears on the back of

her sleeve. Then she sighed and stood up. Might as well get back to Monique and tell her the bad news, she thought. After that, they'd return to the pickup. Monique might complain about her feet the whole way, but they had no choice. They had to get back to the shelter of the little truck.

As she walked, Aletha refused to allow herself to dwell on the worst—that if the rains were heavy enough, even the truck would be a dangerous place. She had heard of vehicles being washed right down the sides of mountains. But she knew they had no choice. For now, the truck was their only hope.

"Aletha," Monique cried when she spotted her niece approaching. "Did you see anyone? Are they sending help?"

Monique looked worse than Aletha had ever seen her look. It wasn't her messy hair and lack of makeup. It was her eyes. They had a wild and crazed look in them.

"I'm sorry, Monique, but I couldn't find anybody," Aletha said. "I walked quite a ways, but there was no sign of a path or trail. Nothing. I came to a section of the forest where there had been a huge fire.

As far as I could see there was nothing but burned trees and scorched brush. It was horrible. But I didn't see any sign of the resort."

"Oh, no," Monique whimpered like a scared child.

"We'd better get back to the pickup," Aletha said. "We don't want to be caught in the rain."

Monique shook her head. "I don't think I can make it back to the truck," she said in a hoarse whisper. Aletha's disappointing news had obviously drained the last of her strength out of her.

"Sure you can," Aletha said. She reached down to take her aunt's hand. "Come on, I'll help you up. You're just a little sore from all this exercise."

Monique sighed heavily. "I'm so tired," she said.

"I am too. I've walked several miles today," Aletha said. "But we've got to get back to the truck no matter what. All of our supplies are in there. Come on. Up you go. I'll help you."

She pulled Monique to her feet and put her hand under her elbow as they started to walk.

"I don't understand," Monique said. "How could this have happened? I just wanted to take you on a nice, fun trip. You're so special to me, Aletha. You're like a daughter to me. I'm closer to you than I am to my own sister. And I had the best of intentions. Why did such a thing happen? Oh, Aletha, why do such terrible things always happen to me?"

Aletha was surprised to hear her aunt talk that way. Monique always had good jobs that paid a lot of money. They were glamorous jobs that took her to far-off places where she met fascinating and important people. She had been around the world many times and always had exciting tales to tell Aletha and her family. What terrible things was she talking about?

"The candidate I worked so hard for lost the election," Monique continued. "The last public relations campaign I ran for that software company failed. Bradley—the love of my life—I'll probably never see him again. And now this!"

"It's like you said before, Monique," Aletha said. "The bad things are the things we end up laughing hardest about when they're over. We'll be laughing about this someday. You'll see."

"My legs ache so much," Monique said. "Couldn't we stop and rest for just a few minutes?"

Suddenly, Aletha heard thunder rumble in the distance. "I don't think we'd better," she replied, glancing at the sky. "I just heard thunder, and the sky is getting darker. If it starts raining, we'll be slipping and sliding through mud. We'd better keep going. Come on. You can do it. One foot in front of the other. That's it."

They trudged on, with Aletha coaxing her aunt along every step of the way.

"Oh, I must look awful," Monique moaned.

"You'll look fine when we get to Swiss Lake," Aletha replied.

"I can just feel my skin sagging," Monique went on. "My hair's a mess. My face is a mess. And look at my shoes. They're filthy!"

"Don't worry about those things now, Monique," Aletha said. "When we get to Swiss Lake, we can have nice, hot showers, and you can put all of your makeup back on. Everything will be fine."

Aletha's words sounded hollow, even to herself. Would they ever get to the resort? she wondered. Right now, Swiss Lake seemed as far away and unreachable as the surface of Mars or Neptune.

Suddenly, a large, cold, wet drop splattered down on Aletha's face.

"Rain!" she gasped.

5 "Hurry, Monique! We're almost there!" Aletha urged as the rain began to beat harder.

"I can't go any faster," Monique protested. "My legs hurt, and my feet hurt. I hurt all over."

"You've *got* to, Monique," Aletha pleaded. "Here. Put your arm around my shoulder. Lean on me while you walk."

She wrapped Monique's arm around her shoulder and began pulling her along now, almost dragging her. Aletha was exhausted herself, and the additional burden of carrying Monique was almost too much.

Then, suddenly, Monique fell. She was on her knees, sobbing. "I *can't* go another step. I just *can't*. Oh, please don't make me go any farther!"

Monique was like a hysterical little girl, pleading beyond reason. And the rain had now become a steady downpour.

Aletha used all of her strength—

strength she didn't even think she had at this point—to pull her aunt to her feet. "There's the pickup," she shouted over the pounding of the rain. "You can make it now."

The two of them stumbled the last few yards and climbed into the cab. They weren't drenched to the skin, but they were pretty wet. Aletha reached into the suitcases and pulled out dry clothing.

"We need to get out of these wet clothes and put on something dry," Aletha said.

Monique pulled off her shirt. She stared at it for a moment. "Look at this! I paid over a hundred dollars for this shirt, and now it's ruined. It's only supposed to be dry-cleaned. I loved this shirt. I bought it at a little boutique in France." She sighed sadly as she pulled on one of the sweatshirts Aletha's mother had packed.

Aletha turned on the radio. "Maybe they're looking for us, Monique. Maybe they'll say something about us being missing. My parents must really be worried by now!"

She dialed in a station in Santa Rosa, not far from where she lived. She knew that if there were any bulletins about them being missing, they would hear them on this station.

After a few minutes, the local news began. Aletha listened impatiently. The newscaster seemed to drone on and on about a holdup at a local convenience store, the city council's decision to approve a new sports center, and other events that had suddenly lost all meaning to Aletha. The only thing that was important to her now was some acknowledgement that someone realized they were missing.

Finally, the newscaster said: *Still no word on the two people missing now for two days. Sixteen-year-old Aletha Dunne and her aunt, Monique Grey, were last seen in a red Toyota pickup, heading for a resort in the Sierra Nevada. The family does not know the exact destination of the pair. Motels, lodges, and resorts throughout the vast Sierra Nevada recreation area are being contacted, but so far none is showing reservations for the pair. Heavy rain is hampering search efforts. Anyone with information about the missing pair is asked to contact the Santa Rosa Police Department.*

"They're looking for us!" Aletha cried.

"Of course they're looking for us," Monique said grumpily. "But finding us is another matter. There are millions of acres in these mountains, and there must be hundreds of roads and trails."

"Yes, but they'll send out search planes," Aletha said.

"Not until the weather clears," Monique pointed out.

"That's all right," Aletha said. "At least they're coming. As soon as the rain stops, I'll build a nice fire that'll draw their attention. And we can make a 'help' sign in that clearing over there. We can pick out our brightest clothes and lay them on the ground to form big letters that they can see from the air."

"All of my beautiful clothing spread out in the mud?" Monique protested.

"We have to, Monique," Aletha said. "We've got to do everything possible to help them find us."

"I guess you're right," Monique sighed.

"It'll break my heart, but I'll do it—as soon as this rain stops."

But the rain only seemed to be getting heavier. Aletha looked out the window to see a small river running alongside the parked pickup. Already the rain had carved out a channel. Brown, dirty water rushed past them like rapids. Again the unthinkable came to Aletha. What if the little river grew? What if it overflowed that narrow channel? Would it carry the truck down into the canyon?

"Oh, I wish the rain would stop," she groaned.

"I've spent my whole life wishing for things," Monique said. "I wished for a job that would give me some satisfaction, but instead all I've ever gotten out of a job is money. I wished for someone to love me with all his heart and soul, and when someone did, I ruined it. Your mom got all those things. Me? I got nothing."

The bitterness in Monique's voice surprised Aletha. She had always thought her aunt enjoyed her wild, carefree life. Why would she ever envy the sister she had always criticized for being too predictable, too levelheaded?

Maybe it was just the fear talking now. But Aletha knew that her mom and dad truly enjoyed their jobs. Nedda Dunne loved teaching third grade at Harriet Tubman Public School. And Aletha's father loved teaching math at the middle school. They also loved each other very much. And they delighted in Aletha.

Could it be that all the time Aletha was looking up to Monique, Monique was looking up to Aletha's mother? Aletha wondered. It didn't seem possible.

An hour later, the rain had lessened a little. But heavy, dark clouds still covered the sky, and a strong wind had come up. Aletha didn't know if the wind was good or bad. She only hoped it would blow the rain clouds away.

The pickup had not been washed into the canyon, though, and that lifted Aletha's spirits somewhat. When she listened to the weather report again, the woman said the storm was moving eastward but that periods of unstable weather would continue for the next 24 hours with the possibility of heavy downpours now and then.

Both Monique and Aletha were exhausted, and for the next several hours, they drifted in and out of sleep, despite the cramped conditions in the cab.

At one point, Aletha awoke and looked at the clock. It was 4:00. The rain was barely coming down now, so she decided she would step out of the pickup and stretch her legs. As she put her hand on the door handle, she glanced out the window. Through the mist, she could see a dark form standing near the edge of the trees. It was tall and shaggy-looking.

She shook Monique's shoulder, awakening her. "Monique, look over there in the trees," she whispered. "Is that . . . a bear?"

"Oh, my gosh," Monique gasped. "It is! I knew it, Aletha! These mountains are crawling with them. It was only a matter of time—"

"Wait!" Aletha cried with relief. "It's not a bear! It's a man! It's a human being, Monique! At last, another human being! Now we can get some help!"

Monique peered out the window. "It *is* a

man," she said. Suddenly her eyes narrowed with suspicion. "Don't get out of the truck, Aletha. We can talk to him from in here."

Aletha took her hand off the door handle. For once, she did not question Monique's instructions. She had heard stories of recluses living in these mountains. They trusted no one, especially people from the government. If they thought someone was spying on them, they could be very dangerous people.

Aletha watched as the man drew closer. He wore a camouflage jacket and pants and knee-high black boots that laced up the front. His beard was long and gray. Under a dirty camouflage cap, his hair hung down like streams of dirty dishwater. He carried a large backpack.

As the man paused by Aletha's door, she rolled her window down an inch.

"Hello," Aletha said, trying to sound friendly. "Are we ever glad to see you!"

The man stared at the pair in the truck. "What are you doing here? What do you want?" he demanded.

Monique sat frozen, obviously incapable of speech.

"We don't want anything," Aletha replied. "Our truck ran out of gas, and we're stranded. You wouldn't happen to have a cell phone, would you?"

"A cell phone?" the man repeated in a growl that would have done justice to a bear. "You think I'm crazy? Those things will fry your brains. It's all a plot. Get everybody to use cell phones, and they'll turn into zombies. Then they'll forget all about their God-given rights, and the government can do whatever it wants. But they ain't getting me into their trap. No way."

"Oh. Um, do you live around here?" Aletha asked.

"You from the government?" the man demanded, his eyes smoldering. Aletha noticed a shotgun sticking out of his backpack. He seemed ready to go for it.

"No, no," Aletha said quickly. "My aunt and I are on vacation. Our truck ran out of gas."

"On vacation? You must be crazy," the man said. "Nobody comes around here on vacation. There's nothing here for spoiled females. You ought to be down at one of those fancy hotels in the city, polluting the atmosphere with your hair dryers and all of your other electrical appliances."

"We just want to get out of here," Aletha said. "Do you have any gas you could sell us? Just enough to get out of here."

"I don't buy and sell nothin'," the man declared. "Money is another tool they use to take away our freedom. But I'll give you a gallon of gas—just to get you out of here."

"That would be wonderful," Aletha said, her heart pounding at the possibility that they were actually going to be able to leave here.

Without another word, the man turned and disappeared into the forest.

Now Monique was able to speak. "Oh, Aletha, do you know what this means? On a gallon we can go 25 miles! That'll take us down the mountain to the other road, the road leading to Swiss Lake. Oh, honey, we're home free!"

Aletha realized that she no longer wanted to go to Swiss Lake. She just wanted to go home. This harrowing adventure was enough to last her all summer! But she couldn't tell Monique that. After all, Aletha had promised to spend two weeks with her aunt, and it wasn't fair to renege on her promise now. And maybe Swiss Lake would be fun. Aletha decided she shouldn't let this bad start ruin everything. The weather was clearing, and tomorrow at this time they'd be swimming or going horseback riding.

About 20 minutes later, the man returned carrying an old beat-up can of gasoline. Without a word, he removed the lid from the truck's tank and poured in the gasoline.

"Start it up!" he commanded Monique.

Monique turned the key, and the truck started. "Yes!" she exclaimed.

As the man started to walk away, Monique took a 20-dollar bill from her purse and rolled down her window a couple of inches. "Here, you've earned this," she said, holding out the bill.

The man spit on the ground between them.

"Filthy money," he growled. "I got no need for it. It's the price of souls. Now get out of here, and don't come back!" He turned then and disappeared into the woods.

"What a strange man," Monique said, returning the money to her purse. "And what strange ideas!"

"You can say that again!" Aletha said. "At least he wasn't dangerous. But we'd better get out of here quick. If he comes back and finds us here, who knows what he'll do."

"You're right." Monique said. She put the truck in gear and stepped on the accelerator. The truck lurched forward a few inches and then stopped as the back tires began to spin.

6   "Put it in four-wheel drive," Aletha suggested.

"This truck doesn't have four-wheel drive," Monique said, hitting the accelerator harder.

"What?!" Aletha cried. "You bought a brand-new truck to take on vacations, and you didn't get four-wheel drive?"

"I never thought I'd need it," Monique protested. The more she hit the accelerator, the faster the wheels spun and the deeper they were stuck. The truck would not move an inch. Monique banged her fists against the steering wheel. "No, no, no!" she cried. "Why is this happening? This isn't fair!"

"Don't panic," Aletha said quickly. "We get stuck when we go camping sometimes, and we just stick something under the back wheels to get traction. Do you have any sand in the back?"

Monique looked at her in surprise. "Sand? No, of course not. I never expected to take this thing off paved roads. Oh, Aletha, we're cursed! Cursed!"

"No, no," Aletha said, grabbing her aunt's arm to calm her. "We can use a piece of the liner in the back of the pickup and stick that under the tires. That'll do it. We can cut two pieces out and stick one under each back tire. That'll give them something to grab on to."

"How are we going to cut that thick liner?" Monique demanded. "With my cuticle scissors?"

"I've got a knife in my suitcase," Aletha said. "Mom packed it with the rest of the stuff." Aletha pulled out the knife and went to the bed of the pickup, hacking out two pieces of the liner. Monique sat in the front seat like a zombie, once again plunged into despair by the setback.

She's no good at all when there's trouble, Aletha thought to herself, remembering all the times her mother had swung into action when a crisis came up. Good old boring Mom knew what to do when the neighbor's child fell into the pool. She was there with CPR. Mom could change a tire, fix a leaky faucet, even retrieve a deleted file from the family's computer. Aletha wished with all her heart that her mother was here now.

Aletha got down in the mud and squeezed the pieces of liner under the back tires, pushing them in as far as she could. Then she stood up. "Okay, Monique. Start it up and accelerate slowly. I'll push from back here."

Monique started the engine, put the truck in drive, and stepped on the accelerator. As the tires spun, Aletha was splattered with mud from head to toe. But the tires grabbed the liners, and the truck gained enough traction to escape the deep mud.

Aletha rushed to the cab and climbed in beside Aunt Monique. "We made it! We made it!" she cried exultantly.

"Whoo—ee!" Monique yelled. "We are *out* of here!" She drove slowly ahead until she could carefully turn around. Then she headed back the way they had come. "Swiss Lake, here we come!"

Aletha wished Monique would keep on driving until they reached civilization. She just wanted to go home now. But Monique was determined to salvage their vacation. And Aletha thought she owed it to her to do the same.

They reached the fork in the road where they had made the wrong turn before. This time Monique turned northeast. The surface of the road was much better than the first one they had taken.

"This is the road to Swiss Lake all right," Monique said. "We're on our way, honey!" She took a quick look at Aletha then and giggled. "Girl, you need a shower!"

Mud splatters covered Aletha's face and clothing, but she didn't care. She knew that soon enough she would be able to take a hot shower, get into clean clothes, and start living like a human being again. All Aletha wanted right now was to see the cabins of Swiss Lake. Then the nightmare they had been living would end.

As they drove on, Aletha noticed that the arrow on the gas gauge was again hovering very near empty.

"Don't worry, honey," Monique said, noticing her niece's glance at the gauge.

"From the way I figure it, we've got about five more miles to the resort. We should be able to make that easily." Suddenly she squealed with delight and pointed out the window. "Aletha, look at that!"

A large sign showing Alpine cabins near a bright blue lake stood on the side of the road. It read: SWISS LAKE—4 MILES.

"Only four miles!" Monique exclaimed. "We're almost there!"

Aletha smiled. She couldn't wait to call her parents. And she could almost feel the hot soapy suds washing away her dirt and grime.

After another mile, another colorful sign advertised the luxuries of Swiss Lake. It showed people diving into pools and feeding deer in meadows. "Gourmet dining" and "mountain fun," the sign offered.

"Oh, honey, just three miles to go!" Monique sang out. The sun had come out, and everything looked bright and hopeful again.

Aletha glanced at the gas gauge again. We must be running on fumes by now, she thought. She crossed her fingers and hoped they would make it all the way to the resort. But even if they had to walk for the last mile or so, it wouldn't be so bad on this nice road in the sunshine.

Still, a small, nagging worry troubled Aletha. Why were there no other cars on this road? Where were the other vacationers? Where were the delivery trucks servicing Swiss Lake?

"Monique, why are we the only people going to Swiss Lake?" Aletha finally asked.

"The bad weather scared everybody away," Monique said. "That means we'll have our choice of cabins. That's a good thing! By the time the nervous Nellies come pouring in, we'll already be settled in."

"But you'd think there would be a few other cars . . ." Aletha said. "At least *one* other car . . . "

The final sign for Swiss Lake promised that the resort was a mile away. At that point, the truck began to sputter.

"Oh, no," Monique moaned. "Come on truck, you can make it one more mile! Just a little bit farther, just a little . . .

Darn!" She pulled onto the shoulder as the truck sputtered to a halt.

"It's okay," Aletha said. "We can walk the last mile easily. We're so close.

"Should we take our suitcases?" Aletha asked as they got out of the truck.

"No, we can have someone at the lodge drive us back for them," Monique said. "Let's just get there."

Monique locked the truck, and they started up the road toward Swiss Lake. They had not walked more than a quarter of a mile when Monique sniffed the air and wrinkled her nose. "What *is* that smell?" she asked.

"Smells like fire. Like an old fire," Aletha said. "I told you that when I walked east from where we were, I saw this big burned area where there must have been a forest fire. Maybe the wind is blowing from that direction, bringing that horrid smell here."

"I wonder how close the fire got to the resort," Monique said. "They must have been scared. I wonder if they had to evacuate all the people."

As they walked, they began to see signs

of the fire right before them. The ground was scorched, and skeletons of dead pines stood as tragic reminders of the flames. It sent a bolt of sadness through Aletha. Such beautiful trees, she thought. It seems such a shame that so many burned. But last year her science teacher had told the class that fire was a natural part of the life cycles of mountain forests. What made the fires so devastating was that humans fought the small fires so successfully that they couldn't do their work of clearing dead brush. Finally, a huge fire would catch on all the dead brush and then just overwhelm everything.

"Aletha, just think," Monique said, "The fire got this close to Swiss Lake! It must have been terrible for the people there. They must have gotten it put out just in time."

Aletha said nothing, but fear suddenly clawed at her. The landscape looked haunted, like a scene from a horror film. Aletha almost expected to see broom-riding witches flying through the sky above the blackened trees. The scorched smell had become pervasive now.

"I'll bet having the fire get this close hurt their business," Monique mused. "That's why we don't see people streaming up here."

Aletha didn't reply. From nervousness, her mouth had suddenly gone very dry. She didn't want to say what was on her mind. She didn't want to think it.

A few minutes later, Monique asked, "Are you as tired as I am, honey?"

"Yeah," was all Aletha could manage to say.

"I hope your folks won't be too mad at me," Monique said. "I mean, not *everything* was my fault . . ."

Aletha knew Monique was waiting for her to agree. Aletha thought, Pretty much everything. You should have gotten gas when we entered the mountains. You forgot the cell phone, not to mention a hundred other things you did wrong. But to Monique, she said, "Mom and Dad are going to be so grateful that we're okay, they won't be mad at anyone."

"I hope so, but I'm not going to count on it," Monique said. "I bet right now Nedda is planning on how she's going to wring my neck. She was always mad at me for something when we were growing up. There was a lot of sibling rivalry between us. I shouldn't be telling you this, and don't you ever repeat it, but your mom was always jealous of me. I think because I was prettier and more popular than she was, and I wasn't afraid to take risks."

Aletha said nothing but thought, if Mom was mad at you all the time, it probably wasn't because you were prettier, Monique. It was probably because of all the *stupid* things you did—just like now!

"Oh, yeah," Monique went on. "I always had the cutest boyfriends. And you know, I always had this . . . this style that turned heads. I don't want to sound conceited, but everywhere we went, people would be looking at me. I put my sister in the shade, and she didn't like it one bit, believe me." Monique laughed sharply. "You wouldn't think it to see me now, all muddy and filthy. But I looked like something special when your mother and I were growing up. All the good-looking young men couldn't take their eyes off me!"

Aletha thought of her father then. He was a really handsome man. He was nice, too, and good-natured and funny and dependable. He was an all-around great guy. He had married Monique's sister. If Monique was so special, why didn't a man like that marry her? Aletha wondered.

Immediately, Aletha was ashamed for having had such spiteful thoughts. Maybe they came to her mind now because she had been through so much with her aunt, she reasoned.

Aletha looked ahead as far as she could see. Why wasn't the landscape changing up there? she wondered. They were almost at Swiss Lake. Why did the fire-scarred landscape continue to surround them? Where had they stopped the conflagration anyway?

Monique had stopped chattering as if she sensed Aletha's sense of foreboding.

A huge sign loomed ahead. It advertised the wonders of Swiss Lake. JUST AHEAD, the big blue letters read. But the sign was charred. There was little left of it.

As the two rounded a bend in the road, the resort came into view.

"Aletha," Monique whispered, reaching out and laying her hand on Aletha's arm. "Aletha . . . " Her voice was full of despair. Ahead they saw a cabin. There was nothing left of it but a chimney and foundation stones piled like rubble.

"Oh, Aletha," Monique was moaning now.

There were more chimneys and charred foundation stones. The chimneys all pointed black fingers to the sky.

Then they saw the lodge. It looked as if it had been bombed. A great chimney stood, and all around the chimney were piles of debris, scorched furniture, bricks, and charred wood.

7

Monique dropped to her knees. She buried her face in her hands and sobbed.

"Please don't cry, Monique," Aletha said. "It's going to be all right." Aletha knelt beside her aunt and put her arm around her shoulders. "It's only a mile back to the truck. It's getting dark, and we can sleep in the truck tonight. In the morning I'll walk back down to the fork in the road and hail somebody."

"We'll never make it out of here!" Monique cried. "There's no way out! Oh, Aletha, what have I done? If I'd have called for reservations, I would have known the place was closed!"

"Let's just get back to the truck," Aletha said, helping her aunt to her feet. "You know what we can do? We can spread out clothing in the bed of the truck to make a nice mattress, and we can stretch a sheet over the top to give us privacy. Why didn't I think of that before? No bugs! And after we get a good night's sleep, things will look much brighter."

Reluctantly, Monique allowed herself to be guided along. They reached the truck at twilight. Aletha hurried to make a comfortable bed in the back of the pickup. Monique stood watching with a glassy look in her eyes.

"We'll both feel better in the morning," Aletha promised as she tucked the sheet under the clothing. Again, she felt as if she were the older of the two, taking care of Monique. She brought out two nutrition bars and some pretzels. They ate silently, changed into clean clothes, and then climbed onto the makeshift mattress.

For a long time neither spoke. Then Monique said, "Aletha, I lied to you about your mother, and I'm sorry. Remember when I said your mom was really jealous of me? How when we'd go someplace, I'd get all the attention and she'd be mad? Well, all that was a lie. The truth is, I was always jealous of *her*. She always had it so . . . together. I mean, she was my little sister, but she got the good grades and had all the nice friends. She had it more together when she was ten than I do now!"

"But, Monique, you've traveled and been in a singing group and worked with famous people," Aletha said.

Monique laughed bitterly. "My singing group stunk. We were awful. Just a bunch of pretty girls with no talent. That's the only reason we got the breaks we did. But after a while, even your looks won't open every door, Aletha."

"But what about all of those glamorous people you met?" Aletha asked.

"They were as phony as I was," Monique said. "Everybody just putting on an act for everyone else. And then, to top it all off, that idiot I campaigned for lost the election. If he'd have won, maybe I would have gotten a meaningful job that I could have been proud of. But, no, he lost!"

"And the travel? I mean, you've traveled the world!" Aletha reminded her.

"Travel's not what it's cracked up to be," Monique replied. "In the end, it's all lines at airports in cities that look the same. Crossing off countries like chores. I did France—good, cross it off. I did

England—okay, cross it off."

"But we had so much fun in Australia," Aletha said. "I mean, just being there gave me goose bumps!"

"Oh, I'm not saying I didn't have fun with *you*," Monique said. "But that was the only reason I liked Australia. Being with you made it special. It was almost like I could be a kid again, everything fresh and fun, because I was seeing it all through your eyes." Her voice turned sad then. "That's why I wanted you on this trip so badly. I was feeling so low about my relationship with Bradley being over that I needed *something*."

Aletha suddenly felt sorry for her aunt. She realized that Monique had been putting on a front her whole life. It must have been very hard at times not to let her guard down. Not to let people see how miserable she really was.

"Well, everything will be okay," Aletha assured her. "Like you said, when this is all over, we'll have something to talk about for a long, long time."

"So you're not angry with me?" Monique asked.

"No, I'm not angry with you," Aletha replied. "We'd better get to sleep now. I've got a long walk tomorrow morning. Good night, Monique."

"Good night, honey," Monique said.

****

Near dawn the next morning, Aletha woke up. Her whole body ached, despite the piles of clothing she had slept on. She dreaded the long walk that lay ahead of her.

"You awake?" Monique whispered.

"Yeah," Aletha said. "I just woke up."

"You know what you said last night about walking back down to the fork for help?" Monique asked.

"Um-hm," Aletha said, sitting up and massaging her legs.

"Well, I've been awake for about an hour, and I've been thinking," Monique continued. "You can't go. It's too dangerous."

Aletha started to protest when Monique raised a finger and said, "Just hear me out. I think we should walk back to the resort. We'll just stay there and make big help signs on the ground. We can use the debris that's strewn around. Search planes will be flying all over these mountains now that the weather has cleared. We've got enough nutrition bars and chips and stuff to stay alive. Maybe we'll even find some nonperishable food at Swiss Lake. There could be a cellar where they stored cans of food, and the fire might have just passed over that."

Surprisingly, Aletha realized she liked the idea. It made sense. Aletha's legs hurt so much, and she was so tired that she wasn't even sure she could make a long hike right now. And, of course, there was always the chance that she might meet a bear on the way . . .

"That's a good idea, Monique," she said.

Monique smiled proudly. "I was hoping you'd say that!" she said. "And we'd better each take a suitcase this time, since we may not be coming back here for a while."

They made a little fire then and had some coffee with a few snacks. Then they each packed one suitcase and started the walk back to the resort. With every step, Aletha was aware of her weariness, despite the night's sleep she had just had. Monique trudged heavily beside her, dragging her wheeled suitcase behind.

When they finally reached Swiss Lake, Aletha noticed the ornamental fake palms that stood around the once-beautiful swimming pool. They were all scorched and twisted from the flames.

"They probably drained the pool after the fire," Monique said. "But maybe it's filled up from the rains. Wouldn't it be wonderful to take a nice long swim and get really clean?"

They hurried toward the pool in spite of their weariness.

"Look," Monique cried, "it's brimming with water from the storm!"

Aletha stared into the pool. The blue and white tiles were charred and discolored, and there was some debris floating around. But the water was generally clean.

"We can take baths, Aletha, *real* baths!" Monique said. "I brought along my soaps and my shampoos. Oh, it'll be so luxurious!"

A few minutes later, the pair was in the

pool, scrubbing away two days' worth of grime. Aletha was so glad to get the mud out of her hair that she almost forgot about the predicament they were in. Afterward, they used what they could find in their suitcases to dry themselves off. Then they put on clean clothes and laid out the damp ones, along with others they had brought, on the grass in the shape of the word HELP.

Monique put on a bright new T-shirt, shorts, and slinky brown sandals. She sat cross-legged on the warm concrete and propped a mirror from her purse on top of a suitcase. Then she began to make up her face. As Aletha watched, she couldn't believe how Monique concentrated as she worked. First she applied her moisturizers and then her foundation. She put on her lip liner, blush, lipstick, and lip gloss. She dabbed green shadow on her eyelids and then carefully separated her eyelashes with a tiny mascara brush. Finally, she brushed and sprayed her hair with regular hairspray. Then she added a coat of spray gloss to make it shine. The whole process took about 45 minutes. When she was finished, she turned to Aletha and said, "How do I look, honey?"

"You look beautiful, Monique," Aletha said, trying not to smile at the futility of her aunt's efforts. After all, who did she think would see her up here?

"We'll make it," Monique declared. "I know now that we are going to be just fine."

Aletha realized that her aunt was like a different person now that she was made up and sprayed down. It was as if she carried around her self-confidence in all those little, expensive bottles and applied it now and then to her soul.

Monique stood up then and said, "Come on. Let's see if there's a cellar under the lodge. Wouldn't it be wonderful if there were all kinds of gourmet foods hiding in some compartment down there?"

They picked their way carefully over the burned brush toward the lodge. They tried to figure out where the kitchen had been. The storage cellar would probably be below the kitchen.

"Monique, look!" Aletha said. "There are all kinds of pots and pans scattered around over there. They must have moved away the big appliances, but I see a lot of utensils."

As the two approached the area, Monique said, "Those stairs there lead down under the kitchen. That must be where they stored the food. Let's go!"

"We'll have to be really careful," Aletha warned. "The stairs could have been weakened by the fire. We'd better go down one at a time so we don't put too much weight on the steps."

Aletha carefully started down the steps, shining the beam of her flashlight into the semidarkness of the cellar below. It looked like Monique had been right. The flames seemed to have raced over the lodge, consuming everything, but the fire hadn't reached the basement.

"I see a lot of shelves on the walls," Aletha said, when she was almost at the bottom of the stairs. "Come on down, but be careful."

As she waited for Monique, Aletha noticed a huge hole in the ceiling. Part of the kitchen floor had collapsed into the cellar. One wall showed evidence of some scorching, but there had been little fuel for the fire from the cement blocks.

"Look, cupboards over there," Monique said. "Maybe that's where they kept the good stuff. Boy, wouldn't it be nice if we could dine in style while we wait to be rescued? Who knows what gourmet delights might be behind those doors?"

They made their way to the cupboards, stepping carefully over the debris.

"You hold the flashlight, and I'll open the door," Monique said eagerly. Aletha pointed her beam at the cupboard door. "I have a feeling we're going to find a treasure trove of food in here!" Monique said, reaching for the handle. But as she pulled open the door, the two froze.

Staring at them was a multitude of tiny red eyes. "Rats!" Monique screamed.

8 Forgetting the possible danger of putting too much weight on the stairs, Monique was gone in a flash. Luckily, the stairs held. Aletha followed a few minutes later after checking out the other cupboards. There were no canned or bottled goods in the cellar. And any bags or boxes of food had been consumed by mice.

"Monique! Come back!" Aletha yelled. "Those weren't rats. They were only mice. They won't bother us now!"

"*Only* mice?" Monique cried, slowing her pace but still moving away from the lodge. "Don't you know those things can bite, girl? We're lucky they didn't go for our throats!"

Aletha started to reply when suddenly she heard something—a distant roar. A plane? she wondered. She searched the sky but could see nothing. Still, the roar was getting louder.

"Monique! A plane! A search plane!" she screamed. "Hurry! Stand by our "help" sign so they see us. Quick!"

Both of them scrambled over to the clothes they had laid out on the ground. They waved their arms wildly at the sky.

"Here! Here!" Monique yelled. "We're down here! Read our sign! *Please!*"

Suddenly the plane appeared out of the clouds. But no sooner did it appear than it disappeared again. Gradually, the roar of the engines faded.

"Did it see us?" Monique asked breathlessly. "Do you think the pilot saw us, Aletha?"

"I don't know," Aletha said. "It may not have even been looking for us. It might have just been some private corporate jet or something."

"Where are the search planes?" Monique demanded. She walked over to her purse, dumping it out again. Then she dug through the contents until she came up with a tiny transistor radio.

"You keep a radio in there too?" Aletha asked. She hadn't seen that the first time.

"Honey, I keep *everything* in here,"

Monique replied. She turned on the radio then, switching from station to station until she found a news broadcast. The signal was weak, but they could just make it out. There was the usual trouble in the hot spots of the world, and locally, two politicians were fighting over the energy situation. Then: *No word yet on the fate of two missing women believed to be somewhere in the Sierra Nevada. Teenager Aletha Dunne and her aunt, Monique Grey, vanished Monday morning while supposedly heading for a resort in the mountains. A search of all motels, hotels, and lodges in the area revealed no one registered by those names. Dunne's mother talked today to reporter Gina Hampton and made this plea to her daughter to come home.*

Aletha gasped. "Does Mom think I've run away?"

Her mother's voice came over the radio then, tearful and shaky. *Aletha, I know you were getting frustrated with the thought of the long summer ahead and that you and your aunt may have made plans you didn't share with us. If you took off for somewhere else, please call us. Your father and I are very worried!*

"Oh, Mom," Aletha moaned. "How could you think I'd do something like that to you and Dad? Why would she think that, Monique?"

Monique chewed her lip for a few seconds before answering. Then she said, "It might be because I . . . ran away once when I was a teenager. Your mom might think you're doing the same thing—with me."

"*What?*" Aletha asked, shocked.

"I was about your age," Monique explained. "You never knew your grandparents, Aletha, but they were even stricter than your parents are. They wouldn't even let Nedda and me date until we were 18. It was awful, at least for me. So once I told them I was spending the weekend with a girlfriend. Instead I flew to Hawaii with this guy who was 21. He was a local rock singer who was just starting to make it big. He thought I was 21 too. Or maybe he just wanted to believe it because I told him I was. Anyway, Mom and Dad never found out, but Nedda did. She was shocked, of course, but she never ratted on me. I was always grateful to her for that. My parents would have grounded me for life. Now that I look back on it, though, I realize they'd have had a right to. It was a really stupid thing to do. In fact, I'm ashamed that I ever did it. Anyway, that might be why your mother is afraid that maybe you've run away."

Aletha tried to put herself in her parents' place. Every time they tried to discipline Aletha, Aletha brought up Aunt Monique and how understanding she was compared to her mom and dad. When Aletha's grades slipped and her dad warned her that she might not get into the college of her choice, Aletha would say, "Monique didn't even go to college, and she has a better life than anybody I know in the whole world!" Once when Aletha had come home late from a party and Mom and Dad had scolded her, Aletha had told them, "I feel like a prisoner here! You guys watch me so closely, like I'm always going to do something wrong! None of my friends have to obey so many rules! I wish

Aunt Monique would ask me to come live with her!"

Aletha realized that her parents had good reason to suspect that she might not be where she was supposed to be!

"Oh, I can't bear to have Mom and Dad think I would do such a thing!" Aletha cried. "Monique, I'm walking out of here *right now*. It's going to be hard, but I *have* to get to a phone so my parents know I'm okay. I can't stand for them to be going through so much worry!"

"Aletha, you can't go," Monique pleaded. "It's too dangerous. If you don't want to think about yourself, then think of me. How would I feel facing your parents when the searchers finally get here and telling them their daughter was killed by a bear—or some mountain man with an attitude?"

"There aren't any bears around here," Aletha snapped. "And mountain man or no mountain man, I'm going. I'm not putting my parents through any more misery. If I make good time, I should reach somebody in three or four hours."

"Aletha, if something happens to you,

your parents will never forgive me. Nedda will hate me forever! My only sister! Our parents are dead. And I have no one in the world except Nedda and her family. Oh, I couldn't bear it. I'd be *totally* alone then." Tears began to stream down Monique's face.

"But we're probably not even going to be rescued," Aletha argued. "They're probably not even looking for us in these mountains. Mom thinks we've run off to Mexico or something. Why should they send search planes all over the Sierra Nevada when they don't even think we're here? Don't you get it, Monique? Are you too dense to understand that?"

Aletha regretted the harshness of her voice immediately but knew she couldn't call it back. She wasn't even sure she really wanted to.

"Please, Aletha," Monique wept. "Don't go."

"I *have* to!" Aletha said. "And I'm going! By tonight I'll be home with my parents."

"Or torn apart by a bear," Monique said.

Aletha ignored her aunt's remark and turned to go.

"All right, okay!" Monique said. "Just wait a minute while I put on my tennis shoes. These sandals will never do. If a bear attacks, at least there'll be two of us fighting him off. And if he wins, then he'll kill us both. And I'd rather be dead than have to face Nedda with you gone!"

"No, Monique," Althea said. "I really don't think you'd be able to make it. You'd just hold me back. Let me go alone, and I'll send back help. You yourself said you're not that young anymore, and you've been through so much in the last two days. I just don't think you could make it."

"Well, I might not be as young as I used to be, but I'm certainly not ready for the nursing home!" Monique cried. "I'm only 38 years old! Why, I could still get married and have children! I—"

"I'm sorry, Aunt Monique," Aletha said. "But I don't have time to stand here arguing with you. I want to make it to the fork before dark."

"Well, I am going with you!" Monique declared. "Let me just find something here to use as a walking stick. I'd use a walker if I had one, but I left mine at home."

Aletha sighed and accepted the fact that her aunt was going with her. "I said I was sorry," she said.

"I don't care what you say. Sorry doesn't change anything," Monique said. "You see me as an old lady, over the hill. You kids are all alike. You think anybody over 30 is a has-been. Well, you just be patient, and in a few years, you'll be my age. Some rude little snip will tell you that you're not young anymore. And when that happens, I hope you'll remember today! Now, let's go. And try to keep up!"

With a bitter expression that no amount of makeup could soften, Monique went over to where she had left her purse lying by the pool. She stuffed a few things into it and marched away. Aletha hurried to catch up.

As they walked, Aletha felt guilty for saying what she had said. In spite of everything that had happened, she loved her aunt. She certainly didn't want to hurt her. After all, Monique had always been a wonderful part of Aletha's life. Even when Aletha was a toddler, Monique had often taken her to the park or the zoo. Monique bought her pinwheels and cotton candy. She told wonderful stories about the elves and fairies. Monique was the funny, flaky, bright friend who was like a rainbow, never dull or drab.

Now, Aletha thought sadly, their special relationship might be coming to an end. Things might never be the same. Monique had been shamed and unmasked during this ordeal. She, the striking beauty, the free spirit, had been reduced to a dirty, weeping, helpless woman who needed reassurance from a 16-year-old.

The last two days had served to remind her that she was not very capable and was even a bit foolish. The remark about her age had been the final straw.

Aletha glanced over at her aunt. She wished she could say something that would make it right again. But she couldn't think of anything. Calling back harsh words was like trying to put toothpaste back into the tube once it had squirted out.

Silently, Monique walked with a grim, determined step as they passed in front of a high cliff, burned black from the fire. Aletha noticed that she looked exhausted, but she was forcing herself to keep pace. Aletha had no doubt that Monique would march on, not pausing to rest even if it killed her. She had been shamed enough. She would be shamed no more.

Suddenly out of nowhere came the hiss of flying gravel. Aletha looked up in confusion.

"Look out!" Monique screamed. She gave Aletha a violent shove that sent her sprawling across the road. The cliff was collapsing!

9 Aletha couldn't hear anything but her own terrified screaming. It filled her ears and her brain. She tried to move, but her legs were buried in an avalanche of dirt. The heavy rains had loosened the burned, ravaged cliff, and it had come down like a heavy beast, rolling over her. She was lying on her back, and when she pulled at her legs, they wouldn't move. In a panic, she screamed again. She looked for Monique but didn't see her. All she could see was mud and chunks of burned cliff all around her.

Finally, she heard Monique's voice in the distance. "Aletha, Aletha!"

Aletha was confused. For a second she thought she was dead and was being buried. Monique was kneeling by her graveside, weeping. But Aletha didn't see her parents or her friends. No one but Monique.

"Aletha, talk to me!" Monique cried. "Oh, please, talk to me!"

Aletha realized then that Monique was beside her, kneeling in the dirt. With her bare hands, she was raking away mounds of dirt with astonishing speed.

Aletha couldn't move her legs, but she could feel the weight of the earth on them. She wondered if they were broken.

"I'm going to get you out, honey," Monique cried. She was throwing dirt in all directions like a crazed dog digging a hole.

"I can't move . . . my legs," Aletha whimpered.

"It's all right, Aletha," Monique assured her. "I'm getting the dirt off. I'm digging you out." Monique was breathing hard, but she kept at it, moving dirt like a machine. Aletha was awed by her aunt's strength. "At least no boulders fell on you, Aletha. We were spared that. Oh, this is all my fault!"

"No," Aletha whispered. "You wanted to wait for the rescue planes up at the resort."

"Just a little more, just a little more," Monique said, still digging frantically. Aletha could see blood running from her fingers to her wrist. But Monique seemed oblivious to it. She worked in a frenzy.

Aletha wiggled her toes on her left foot. Then she did the same with her right foot. "I can move both legs a little," she said.

Monique hurried to get behind Aletha. She reached under her arms and dragged her out of the landslide. She lifted Aletha from the earth prison and hauled her across the road, beyond the reach of the crumbling mountain.

Then Monique knelt down beside Aletha and looked at her legs. She gently moved them, asking Aletha if this hurt or that hurt.

"They're pretty sore," Aletha said. "I don't think I can walk without help."

"Come on, honey," Monique said, "I'll help you up. You lean on me. We're going over in that clearing over there. I don't trust that mountain."

They walked slowly into the clearing and sat down on an old log. Aletha was getting over the shock of almost being buried alive.

"Monique, I was almost killed!" Aletha said. "If you hadn't pushed me, I would have been buried alive!"

Suddenly a huge rock broke away from the cliff and fell. It landed on the exact spot Aletha had been buried. Aletha looked at her aunt. "If you hadn't gotten me out of there, that rock would have fallen on me! You . . . you saved my life!" Tears poured down her face.

"Shhh, it's okay now," Monique said. She took Aletha in her arms and held her until she stopped crying.

"Oh, Monique, what's going to happen to us?" Aletha moaned. "We'll never make it to the fork now. I'd never be able to walk that far. What will we do?"

"Well, for starters, we're going to have to sleep in the open here tonight," Monique said. "Then we'll try to make it to the fork tomorrow. If your legs are too sore, I'll go alone."

"Alone?" Aletha asked, surprised. "You'd go alone?"

"If I have to, I will," Monique said. "It might be our only choice." She stood up then. "Now I've got to get busy and make a fire. It'll be cold tonight, especially sleeping out here in the open."

"But, Monique, the matches," Aletha

said. "I didn't bring them with me when we left the resort."

Monique smiled and dug in her purse. "Ta-dah!" she beamed, holding up the box of matches. "I grabbed them right before we left. I also grabbed the last of the nutrition bars and the end of the pretzels. It might not be gourmet food, but at least we won't starve."

"You are amazing!" Aletha laughed.

A few minutes later, Monique had a nice fire going. Darkness had fallen fast, and Aletha was grateful for the warmth and for the light. They ate their meager supper then and lay down on the ground. Monique insisted that Aletha use her huge leather purse for a pillow. "You go ahead," she said. "I'm going to stay up and keep the fire going. You never know when one of those bears might show up."

"Or a spider," Aletha laughed. "You really *are* amazing. You're the one who's going to get us through this, Monique."

"*Aunt* Monique," Monique said. "Call me Aunt Monique. After all, that's what I am. It's about time I stopped trying to be something I'm not."

Aletha smiled and said, "Aunt Monique. I like that better. I think Mom and Dad will like it too." Mentioning her parents reminded her how much she missed them. "I just wish I could get word to Mom and Dad that I'm okay and that I love them," she sighed.

Monique smiled then and said, "Tell you what, honey. You think of your mom and dad now with all your heart. You think about them so hard that your head feels like it will burst."

"What good will that do?" Aletha asked doubtfully.

"I had an uncle once who went to war, and his wife worried a lot about him," Monique explained. "But every night he'd think about her, and she'd know that he was all right. It was like their hearts were speaking to each other over all that distance. He did that all through the war. And even once when he was injured and almost died, his wife knew he was all right. Now you close your eyes, and for the next minute, think real hard about your mom and dad."

Aletha did as Monique told her, though she wasn't sure there was anything to it. She closed her eyes and repeated in her mind, "Mom, Dad, I'm okay. I love you. And I hope I'm coming home soon."

10 In the morning, a distant roar in the sky roused Aletha and Monique. Both looked up at once.

"It's a small plane, Monique!" Aletha screamed. "It must be one of the search planes looking for us!"

Monique had kept the fire going, but they had made no help signs in the area. "Build the fire higher, Aletha!" Monique said. "Put some more of those sticks on!"

Then Monique ran into the middle of the meadow and began waving her arms wildly. No trees obscured them. But Aletha wasn't sure that the fire would attract attention in the daylight or that they could be seen from the altitude of the plane.

"Do you think the pilot sees us?" Aletha cried as she shoved sticks into the flames.

"I don't know," Monique called back. "He seems to be circling. Maybe it's just someone out for a morning flight. Maybe he doesn't even know about us."

The small plane seemed to be coming in for a closer look, but maybe that was just wishful thinking. Monique continued to wave her arms and, at one point, even grabbed her purse and waved that too.

"He's going away," she finally said in a disappointed voice. "I don't think he was even searching for us at all. He was just out for a ride in his plane."

"Maybe he saw us," Aletha said hopefully. "Maybe he'll call in and say he saw us, and then they'll send someone up the road to look for us. A plane couldn't land around here anyway. Too many cliffs and rocks. He might've seen us."

"Maybe," Monique said. "Maybe. How are you doing this morning? Can you walk?"

Aletha stood then and tested her legs. "I think they're more stiff from sleeping on the hard ground all night than sore," she said. She walked tentatively around the little campsite. "They seem to be fine. I think the more I move, the better they'll get."

"Think you can make it to the fork?" Monique asked.

"I'll try," Aletha said. "I might not move very fast, but I think I can make it."

"Need a walking stick, Granny?" Monique teased.

Aletha laughed. "As a matter of fact, I think that's exactly what I need." She reached into the pile of wood Monique had gathered for the fire. "Here's a good one," she said, picking up a stick about four feet long. "Let's go, you young whippersnapper!" she said in her best grandmotherly voice.

They continued their trek then, slowly walking down the road and making sure they didn't get too close to the unstable cliffs.

"Aunt Monique," Aletha said as they walked, "I don't want to be nosy. But why wouldn't you marry Bradley Simms?"

Monique shrugged. "To tell you the truth, I'm not sure I've figured that out," she said. "I *told* him I wasn't ready to get married. That I had a few more exciting things I wanted to do. But I've been thinking about it a lot lately, and I don't think that was why."

"Why, then?" Aletha asked.

"I think deep down I knew that if I got married, that would be the end of a part of me," Monique said. "My youthful part, I guess. As a married woman, I wouldn't be anyone special anymore. Monique the glamorous adventuress would no longer exist. And in her place would be plain old Mrs. Bradley Simms. Marrying Bradley would have been admitting that I was getting older. And I wasn't ready to do that yet."

"Are you ready to do that now?" Aletha asked quietly.

Monique started to speak, but before she could they both heard another rumble.

"What is that?" Aletha asked fearfully. "Oh, Aunt Monique, do you think it's another cliff collapsing somewhere?" She looked around wildly for the beginning of another landslide.

Suddenly Monique yelled, "Look, Aletha! Look what's coming up the road!"

From around the bend in the road, a big sport utility vehicle carrying two men appeared. On the door was a large badge decal with "Sheriff" written on it. Stunned, Aletha and Monique waited as the SUV rumbled right up to them and stopped. A young man with close-cropped hair jumped out of the passenger seat. "Are you Aletha Dunne and Monique Grey?"

"Yes!" they both screamed at once.

"We're from the Santa Rosa sheriff's department," he said. "I'm Deputy Roberts. This is Deputy Vargas. The pilot of a search plane alerted us to two ladies in a meadow up here."

"He saw us, Aletha!" Monique exclaimed. "That pilot saw us! Oh, bless that man! What is his name? I want to thank him personally. Oh, what a wonderful man!"

"Let's see here," the young man said, consulting a small notepad. "A Mr. Bradley Simms, local pilot, radioed in at 8:07 this morning."

"Bradley?" Monique cried. "Oh, my precious Bradley! He saved us, Aletha! Bradley saved us! Can you believe that?"

"I can believe it, Aunt Monique," Aletha said. "Bradley loves you. He'd do anything he could to rescue you if he thought you were in trouble."

Tears came to Monique's eyes then. "Bradley—my knight in shining armor," she sighed.

"You ladies better get into the SUV," the young man said. "You look like you've been through a lot."

Immediately Monique reached up to smooth her hair. "Oh, I must look like a crone, an old crone," she began. "I don't normally look like . . ." She stopped then and looked at Aletha. "What *am* I saying?" she said. Then she added, "Young man, we look like we've been through a lot because we *have* been through a lot. *You* try walking around these ridiculous mountains for three days. Honey, it would make *anyone* old!"

"Yes, ma'am," the young man said. He helped them into the back seat of the SUV and handed each a bottle of water.

"Can I call my parents?" Aletha asked as they headed down the mountain.

"No problem," the young man said.

Within minutes Aletha was on the phone with her mother. She was so happy to hear her mother's voice that she almost shouted into the phone. "Mom! We're okay. We broke down in the mountains, but we're fine. We heard you on the radio. I'm sorry you were so worried!"

"Aletha!" her mom cried. "Oh, Aletha! Is that really you? Are you sure you're all right?"

"We're fine, Mom," Aletha replied. "We broke down and walked for miles and just about everything went wrong. But you know what? Aunt Monique was wonderful! She saved my life in a landslide. I'll tell you all about it when we get home. I can hardly wait to see you, Mom. I love you. And tell Dad I love him too."

As Aletha handed the phone back to the young man in the front seat, she saw that Monique was watching her closely. "What's wrong, Aunt Monique?" Aletha asked.

"Oh, honey, you didn't tell your mother the truth," Monique replied. "You need to tell her what a fool I was up there . . . All those things I did wrong, those bad decisions I made . . ."

"The *truth* is that you saved my life, Aunt Monique," Aletha said, giving her aunt a hug. "That's all that matters."

Monique was quiet for a moment. Then she said, "You know, I never got a chance to answer that question you asked me back there."

"What question?" Aletha wanted to know.

"Whether I was ready to become Mrs. Bradley Simms," Monique replied.

"Are you?" Aletha asked.

Monique smiled then and said, "I've never been more ready for anything in my life."

Aletha smiled too. She liked the idea of having both an Aunt Monique and an Uncle Bradley.

****

Aletha's mother told her soon after she got home that the night before the rescue, she was lying awake crying. But suddenly she felt a tremendous sense of peace. She knew somehow that Aletha was all right.

"It was when I sent my love to you," Aletha said.

Before the summer was over, Aletha went on another trip, this time with her family. In August, the Dunnes traveled to the Canadian Rockies for a week of camping. Her parents had decided that it was time to go a little farther than 100 miles away from home. Uncle Bradley and Aunt Monique came too. Aletha had been maid of honor at their wedding in July.